GARFIELD
WORDS OF WISDOM

JIM DAVIS

RAVETTE BOOKS

First published by Ravette Books Limited 1992

Printed and bound for
Ravette Books Limited
3 Glenside Estate, Star Road, Partridge Green,
Horsham, West Sussex RH13 8RA
An Egmont Company
by Proost International Bookproduction, Belgium

ISBN: 1 85304 401 6

GARFIELD
A bit over the top

Toast Of The Town

Get Your Skates On!

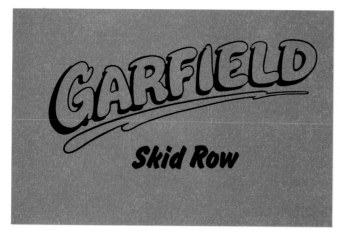

Pas
de
Deux

Slapstick comedy

Tiptoe through the tulips

I DON'T KNOW WHAT GOT INTO MY CAT! I'M REALLY SORRY!

NONSENSE! THAT'S THE MOST EXERCISE REBA'S HAD IN YEARS!

Nappy days are here again

Beware of inflation

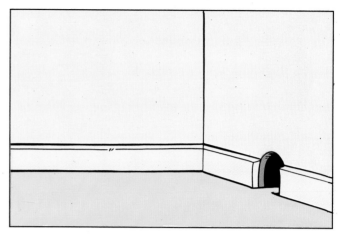

MUNCH MUNCH MUNCH

© 1989 United Feature Syndicate, Inc.

MUNCH MUNCH MUNCH

JIM DAVIS

4-30

WOOSH WOOSH WOOSH WOOSH WOOSH WOOSH

Licked again

WOW: JELLY BEANS! I LOVE JELLY BEANS!

© 1989 United Feature Syndicate, Inc.

JIM DAVIS   5-21

SLURP!

The Private Eye

THIS IS A STORY ABOUT HIGH HOPES DASHED IN THE BIG CITY...

IT'S NOT A PRETTY STORY, BUT... I'M NOT A PRETTY CAT...

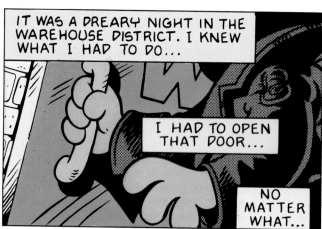

IT WAS A DREARY NIGHT IN THE WAREHOUSE DISTRICT. I KNEW WHAT I HAD TO DO...

I HAD TO OPEN THAT DOOR...

NO MATTER WHAT...

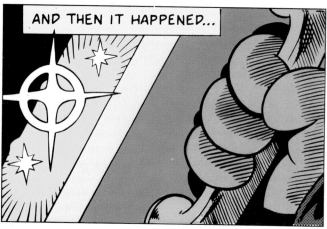

AND THEN IT HAPPENED...

GASP!

© 1989 United Feature Syndicate, Inc.

I HAD COME THIS CLOSE TO MY BIG DRAMATIC DEBUT

5-28

JIM DAVIS

Surfin' USA

The Birthday Boy

Cracking up

© 1989 United Feature Syndicate, Inc.

JIM DAVIS

6-18

OTHER TITLES AVAILABLE IN THIS SERIES

GARFIELD

No. 1 Sitting Pretty

HAGAR

No. 1 The Hero

LUCKY LUKE

No. 1 The Dalton Brothers
        Memory Game

MARMADUKE

No. 1 Canine Capers

PINK PANTHER

No. 1 Through The Hoop

SNOOPY

No. 1 Swings Into Action

THUNDERBIRDS

No. 1 To The Rescue
No. 2 In Space

TOM & JERRY

No. 1 Copy Cat
No. 2 Sweet Temptation

£3.99 each

Additional titles will be added to this series, for a complete list please contact
Ravette Books.

All these books are available at your local bookshop or newsagent, or can be ordered
direct from the publisher. Just tick the titles you require and fill in the form below. Prices
and availability subject to change without notice.

Ravette Books Limited, 3 Glenside Estate, Star Road, Partridge Green, Horsham,
West Sussex RH13 8RA

Please send a cheque or postal order and allow the following for postage and packing.
UK – 50p for one book and 35p for each additional book ordered.

Name ....

Address ....

....